BACH TWO AND THREE PART INVENTIONS · ALEXANDER AND LOFTHOUSE

DISTRIBUTED IN CANADA BY

ALGORD MUSIC LIMITED

372A YONGE ST., TORONTO

Printed in England.

Publisher's Note:—

The border used on the cover of this work, was designed by Irene M. Lofthouse and based on an engraving-
probably the work of Wilhelm Friedemann Bach – to be found in the original edition of The Art of Fugue, *1751*

Auffrichtige Anleitung,

Wormit denen Liebhabern des Clavires,
besonders aber denen Lehrbegierigen, eine deut=
liche Art gezeiget wird, nicht alleine mit 2 Stimmen
reine spielen zu lernen, sondern auch bey weitern pro=
greßen auch (2) mit dreyen obligaten Partien richtig
und wohl zu verfahren, anbey auch zugleich gute inven=
tiones nicht alleine zu bekommen, sondern auch selbige gut
durchzuführen, am allermeisten aber eine cantable
Art im Spielen zu erlangen, und darneben einen
starcken Vorschmack von der Composition zu über=
kommen.

Verfertiget

von
Joh: Seb: Bach.
Hochfürstlich Anhalt=Cöth=
nischen Capellmeister,

Anno Christi 1723.

BACH'S TWO AND THREE-PART INVENTIONS

Introduction

What could be more illuminating than Bach's dedicatory title to the Two and Three-Part Inventions, written in 1723 in his own hand, in the following words :—

"An honest guide, wherewith lovers of the clavier, and especially those anxious to learn, are shown a clear method not only how to learn to play neatly in two parts, but further to play correctly and well in three obbligato parts ; and at the same time not only to acquire good *inventiones* [ideas] but to work them out well ; but above all to attain a cantabile style of playing, and in addition to get a strong taste for composition ". *

In the Little Clavier Book written by Bach for his son Wilhelm Friedemann in 1720 the Inventions first appeared under the title of " Præambulum " and " Fantasia " ; in a later copy they were entitled " Invention " and " Sinfonia ".

We now know that the Inventions were intended to be played on the clavichord, an instrument capable of the most delicate nuances. It is of interest to know that Bach preferred the clavichord to the harpsichord because he said he could make this instrument sing. The action of the clavichord teaches us to play with a light touch and to give the notes time to tell. This lightness of touch and control of pace we must try to acquire on the piano ; it will help particularly with the gracing of the notes.

Our study of the music of Bach requires an " inward eye ". Slowly but surely, as we look and play, fresh beauties will be revealed to us. Great enjoyment can be found in the playing of these works.

To play is to know : to know is to analyse.

The accompanying notes are not designed to form a comprehensive analysis, rather they are sign-posts pointing the way to enjoyment and understanding.

C. Thornton Lofthouse

* English translation by Ernest Newman from " J. S. Bach " by Albert Schweitzer (A. & C. Black Ltd.)

The Two-part Inventions

INVENTION No. 1 in C major (p.18)

The form of this Invention is compact and concise. It springs from the following motif :—

The invention divides into three sections. In section one, bars 1 – 7, the motif is treated in imitation. In section two, bars 7 – 15, the order of entries is reversed and use is made of inverse motion. In section three, bars 15 – 22, the entries appear alternately in inverse and direct motion. Further use is made of inverse motion in passages of a sequential character, e.g. bars 3 – 4 and 11 – 12.

The playing of this invention requires a flowing rhythm and an alert touch. The final chord may be spread as shown in the autograph copy.

INVENTION No. 2 in C minor (p.20)

This is a thoughtful, almost wistful piece of music. The wide *tessitura* of the parts, together with the leaps, gives it a definite appeal and expressiveness. Its make-up deserves our attention, for here surely is a case of art concealing art. If we play the right-hand part as far as bar 9, then the left-hand part as far as bar 11, it will be seen that the two are in canon at the octave with the right hand leading. At bar 11 the key-centre has now changed to G minor and the position of the parts is reversed, the left hand leading in canon with the right hand entering at bar 13. A link leads to the return to the tonic key at bar 23, in which the right hand has the theme with the counter subject in the left hand. These positions are reversed at bar 25.

Legato playing is required of the performer and neat treatment of the mordents in the counter-subject.

INVENTION No. 3 in D major (p.22)

Invention No. 3 in D major is of a cheerful and conversational character and consists of free imitation.

Note should be taken of bars 10 – 11, where Bach superimposes on the existing time-plan three bars of $\frac{3}{8}$ in a bar : —

This superimposition of the rhythm occurs at bars 22 – 23, leading to the cadence in B minor, at bars 36 – 37, leading to the cadence in A major, and at the close, bars 57 – 58. A device of this kind is typical of 18th century music. For further examples, see the aria "Jesus, Saviour" from Bach's *St. Matthew Passion* and the air "I know that my Redeemer liveth" from Handel's *Messiah*.

In the autograph copy this invention is one of the few in which the phrasing is shown.

INVENTION No. 4 in D minor (p.24)

This invention is built on the following motif which is treated now in direct, now in inverse motion :—

motif

The first section ends with a cadence in the key of the relative major (bars 17 - 18). A return to the opening motive with its accompanying counter-subject occurs at bar 44. As in the previous invention, there is a superimposition of the rhythm in bars 16 - 17, bars 36 - 37, leading to the cadence in A minor, and at bars 47 - 48 and 50 - 51.

INVENTION No.5 in E flat major (p.26)

Who amongst us does not love a long tune to play or to listen to? For those who do, this invention, with its themes in invertible counterpoint is a happy experience. An added glow that contributes to the general effect is the inclusion of the grace-notes.

The episodes that separate the main appearances of the theme are ingeniously contrived, being culled from material of the opening bar.

The tonal trend of the parts in the closing section gives a sense of unexpectedness to the ending. However, home is sighted just in time for the final cadence.

In performance a *cantabile* treatment of the tune will enable it to stand out in contrast to its companion.

INVENTION No. 6 in E major (p.28)

Invention No. 6 in E major is interesting for the fact that it is the only one of the series to have double-bars and repeat signs, similar to those found in the movements from the Suites. Though written in a "binary" framework, it produces a "ternary" effect. The opening four bars make play on a scale in contrary motion and in syncopation. This idea forms the basis of the composition:—

The theme with its counter-subject is in invertible counterpoint. Of special interest is the figure in bar 4 of the counter-subject; this is used to form an extended episodical passage in bars 9 - 18. Bars 18 - 20 form a delightful coda. After the double-bar, bars 21 - 28 are in the dominant key and should be compared with bars 1 - 8. There follows a longish development of the figure in bar 4, after which the music returns to the tonic key at bar 43 with the opening statement shown in reverse position. Bars 60 - 62 form the final coda and should be compared with bars 18 - 20.

INVENTION No. 7 in E minor (p.30)

This invention bears a resemblance to No. 1 in C major, though its expression is different. The right hand leads off with the following motif:—

This is followed by an episode ending with a cadence in the key of the relative major (bars 6 – 7). The middle section contains further development of the opening figure, with modulations to D major (bar 9) and B minor (bar 13). A dominant pedal leads to the concluding section.

The speed of the playing of the grace-notes should depend upon the particular mood. The mood of this piece is a wistful one and to retain it, the grace-notes should not be hurried.

INVENTION No. 8 in F major (p.32)

This particularly happy invention is based on an ascending broken chord figure:—

It is "binary" in form. Section I (bars 1 – 12) begins in canon at the octave and modulates to the key of the dominant.   Section II (bars 12–34) is the longer of the two halves and in the course of its development touches upon various related keys.   Bars 26–34 are interesting as they are an exact transposition a fifth lower of bars 4 – 12.

INVENTION No. 9 in F minor (p.34)

Fugal in style, this invention has a subject of four bars in length. The accompanying counter-subject is in double counterpoint:—

At bar 5 the parts interchange. Contracted and expanded versions of the subject and counter-subject lead to a cadence in the dominant key (bars 16–17). At this point, the subject is presented in the bass with the counter-subject in the treble. An episode based on the following figures leads to the final appearance of the subject and its counter-subject in bar 29:—

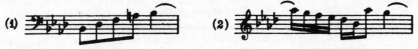

The effect of the rhythm is flowing and continuous. The wide *tessitura* of the parts gives an added intensity and poignancy to the character of the music.

INVENTION No. 10 in G major (p.36)

This invention has that gaiety of rhythm and transparency of texture that is found in Bach's *Fugue à la Gigue*. It is full of harmonic implications and the student would do well to gather together the notes that combine to make the chord progressions. By so doing, the ingenuity contrived by such simple means will at once be apparent; further, an insight will be gained into the many sequences that abound in this short and sparkling piece of music.

It begins like a fugue with this theme which is taken up by the bass in bar 2:—

Section II, bar 14, starts in the dominant key with the entry of the parts reversed. The return is made in bar 27 where the right hand has the tune, and where increased interest is brought about by the left hand entering with the theme in close imitation at the distance of a quaver beat.

It should be remembered that the purpose of a trill is to carry on the melodic line. Therefore the tone need not be even throughout but graded so that it helps the flow of the rhythm.

INVENTION No. 11 in G minor (p.38)

This invention is built upon the following theme and its accompanying counter-subject:—

Note should be taken of the chromatic character of the counter-subject. Both themes are capable of development and extension, e.g. bars 7–11 where the music leads to the "half-way house" in the dominant key, and bars 18 – 23 which contain the final appearance of the theme. Shortened and inverted appearances of the counter-subject are seen in bars 4 – 5 and 14 – 15. Material from both themes form short episodes, as in bars 5 – 6.

INVENTION No. 12 in A major (p.40)

This invention is of a flowing and pastoral nature with its time signature of $\frac{12}{8}$. It is in the style of a fugue having the following subject and accompanying counter-subject:—

Bars 1 – 4 constitute the exposition. The tunes in bars 3 – 4 are reversed and the music is in the dominant key. Then follows an episode of a sequential nature built on the opening material, with an extension in bars 7 – 8. Middle entries occur in the keys of F sharp minor (bars 9 – 10) and C sharp minor (bars 11 – 12). A second episode (bars 13 – 17) leads to the final appearance of the tune in the tonic key (bars 18 – 19).

INVENTION No. 13 in A minor (p.42)

This invention has the character of a prelude and is built upon the following motif :—

Bars 1 – 6 constitute the first section, ending with a full close in C major.   Section two commences with the motif in the left hand and concludes with a cadence in E minor (bar 13). A decorative passage built on chords of the diminished seventh leads to a return to the tonic key, with the right hand entering with the tune as in bar one.

This is an exacting invention to play as semiquaver movement is maintained throughout. The student would do well to make an analysis of the chords and play them in close formation, e.g. :—

(Bars 1 & 2)

By so doing, the player will be able to get an overall technical grip of the notes and a feeling for the line and shape of the music.

INVENTION No. 14 in B flat major (p.44)

This invention, like No. 13 in A minor, is in the form of a prelude.   It is based on the motif:—

The opening statement (bars 1 – 4) leads to a short episode on fragments of the motif and its inversion treated antiphonally (bars 4 – 5).   At bar 6, the parts are inverted and in a key a fifth higher.   Bars 9 – 16 form an extended episode and are in the nature of a development. A return to the opening idea is made at bar 16, where the tune is in canon at the distance of one crotchet beat.   For further use of canonic treatment, see bars 12 – 13.

As in Invention No. 13, the student will gain much help if the notes that form the chords are played in close formation, e.g. :—

(Bars 1-4)

INVENTION No. 15 in B minor (p.46)

A most unusual opening. To a theme of two bars is added a bass in quavers. The latter has all the appearance of a continuo part. The answer is in the key of the dominant and is accompanied by a counter-subject (bars 3 – 5). A further appearance of the theme leads to an episode (bars 8 - 12). This episode is treated sequentially from material found in the counter-subject and comes to a close in the key of the relative major. Middle entries of the theme appear in the keys of the relative major and its dominant (bars 12 - 13 and 14 - 15). A second episode (bars 16 – 18) leads to final appearances of the theme in bars 18 – 19 and 20 - 21.

A quality of dry humour is to be found in this invention which needs to be treated with exactness and precision. In the episodes there is delightful contrast which requires *legato* treatment.

Rarely is phrasing shown in the autograph copy, but a few phrase-marks are indicated in this invention.

The Three – part Inventions (Sinfonia)

INVENTION (Sinfonia) No. 1 in C major (p.48)

The student is advised to play the invention that is in the same key and then play Sinfonia No. 1. It will be found that the two are cast in the same mould, but the effect produced by the latter is of an added richness.

Contained in the opening bar are the germs from which the sinfonia springs :—

The theme in its inverted form :—

INVENTION (Sinfonia) No. 2 in C minor (p.50)

This sinfonia is built on the above theme, but only in four instances do we get the theme in its entirety. These are in the soprano and alto voices in the exposition, and later in a group of entries centred round the dominant key in the bass and soprano (bars 9 and 11). What appear to be entries at bar 5 in the bass, and bar 13 in the alto, are curtailed —see motif (a) and combine to form episodical sequences in triple counterpoint. The second half of the sinfonia (bar 19 to the end) is a development of material from bar 5 and is more in the character of a fantasia.

INVENTION (Sinfonia) No. 3 in D major (p.52)

A comparison should be made of this sinfonia with the invention in the same key. Both bear the same clear-cut character.

The theme is three bars in length :—

Three entries of the theme comprise the exposition. A short episode (bars 8 – 9) leads to an entry of the theme in the relative minor (bars 10 – 12). A further episode concludes with a cadence in F sharp minor (bars 12 – 14). Here follows considerable play of the opening motif in stretto. The final entries are three in number, the first in the key of the sub-dominant (bars 19 - 21) and the last two in the tonic key (bars 21 – 23 and 23 – 25). Note should be taken of bars 3 – 5 which are written in triple counterpoint, and comparison made with bars 6 – 8 and elswhere. It will be seen with what economy of material these are devised :—

INVENTION (Sinfonia) No. 4 in D minor (p.54)

The playing of this sinfonia demands a real feeling for line, therefore care must be taken to see that each note is so adjusted as to take its proper place in the phrase. This sinfonia needs to be played with a quiet mind and an easy rhythm. Bach at the end of each half produces a master phrase (bars 12 – 13 and 22 – 23).

The theme with its counter-subject is as follows :—

INVENTION (Sinfonia) No. 5 in E flat major (p.56)

This sinfonia is of transcendent beauty and repose. It is worth studying for the perfection of its phrases alone and for its feeling for key. A comparison should be made with the slow movement from the Brandenburg Concerto No. 6 in B flat. The two upper parts are written in free canon form, while the bass repeats the same figure in each bar.

Imagine the music played by a string trio and you will realise the need to make each part sing. Translate this idea into terms of the keyboard and you will get the effect that is desired.

INVENTION (Sinfonia) No. 6 in E major (p.58)

Of a pastoral and flowing character, this sinfonia has for its time-signature ⁹⁄₈. The theme on which the work is based is :—

In the course of the work it appears by inversion. The "half-way house" is at the cadence in B major in bars 17 – 18. After a somewhat vigorous concluding section, the music comes to a rest with a graceful double suspension.

INVENTION (Sinfonia) No. 7 in E minor (p.60)

Sinfonia No. 7 in E minor is built upon the following theme :—

It is particularly euphonious in character, its parts moving in thirds and sixths. It would make a good trio for strings or wind. Contrapuntally, the opening section (bars 1 – 14) moves mainly note against note, but semiquaver movement is also suggested. After the cadence in B minor (bars 13 – 14), more flow is given to the music by the employment of continuous semiquaver movement until the return to the opening key in bar 37. This expressive and noble sinfonia ends with a cadence which employs a *Tierce de Picardie.*

INVENTION (Sinfonia) No. 8 in F major (p.62)

In the twenty-three bars which comprise Sinfonia No. 8 in F there are twenty-one appearances of the theme, and only four bars where the theme is absent. The theme is of one bar's duration :—

The counter-subject is shown as it accompanies the theme on each of its appearances in the exposition ; further, it helps to indicate the modulations to the dominant and supertonic keys (bars 7 and 11). Short episodes derived from the theme occur in bars 4 – 5, 16 – 17 and 20. In the middle group of entries the theme is used in stretto.

INVENTION (Sinfonia) No. 9 in F minor (p.64)

Never was more meaning and poignancy packed into the thirty-five bars that comprise this sinfonia. It is one of the rare movements in Bach's music, comparable with "The Lament of his friends" from the *Capriccio on the departure of his beloved brother.*

The piece consists of three themes in triple counterpoint. Although in contrast to one another, these themes express the same particular emotion :—

After the entrance of themes one and two they are joined by theme three, and in four differing ways of presentation they combine together to make nine different appearances. Contrast is provided by five interludes, of which the first is free in form, the others being derived from theme one. Use is made of direct and inverse motion and augmentation in creating this complex effect.

The only three phrase-marks in the autograph copy are shown in the examples given above. They throw light on the whole treatment.

INVENTION (Sinfonia) No. 10 in G major (p.66)

The Sinfonia is built upon the following theme :—

The exposition ends at bar 9. Varied appearances of the theme forming what might be termed middle entries appear between bars 11 and 26. The final section commences at bar 26. The following figures are significant :—

which appears at cadence points, such as the one at bars 4 - 5.

which is used later to form sequential episodes, as in bars 9 - 10 and 17 - 19.

The student should analyse the sinfonia carefully for the appearances of the theme, and decide whether the entries are real or whether they are intended to be more in the nature of episodes.

This sinfonia has a flowing quality and demands an urgent rhythm. It ends with a feeling of triumph.

INVENTION (Sinfonia) No. 11 in G minor (p.68)

This sinfonia opens with a phrase eight bars in length, answered by a corresponding one ending with a cadence in the key of the relative major (bars 15 – 16). The section that follows is sequential in character and leads to the " half-way house " with a modulation to the dominant key (bars 35 – 36). The second half is treated in the form of a development and concludes with a restatement of the opening phrase (bars 65 – 72). Note should be taken of the pedal point in bars 24 – 29, and a comparison made with that on the dominant pedal (bars 57 – 64). This sinfonia has an aria-like quality and should be made to sing. It is interesting to note the use Bach makes of successive chords of the seventh, e.g. bars 17 – 21.

INVENTION (Sinfonia) No. 12 in A major (p.70)

This sinfonia is as clear-cut as it is well balanced. There are three entries of the theme in the exposition, and a fourth entry for those who might be less quick in the up-take. This is followed by an episode of some length containing a pedal-point leading to the one entry in the middle section. Another episode, balancing the first, leads to a return to the tonic key with entries in the bass and soprano. The work ends delightfully unexpectedly leaving something to the imagination. The whole is cheerful in character and requires a precise and light touch to make the music sparkle.

INVENTION (Sinfonia) No. 13 in A minor (p.72)

It is interesting to compare the sinfonia in A minor with the invention of the same key. The latter is busy and the rhythms generally keep to a formal plan. Here the music is more thoughtful, perhaps due to the stepwise nature of the tune (bars 1 – 4). The movement of the parts in thirds and sixths gives a particularly euphonistic effect. Touches of humour are added by the introduction of a new counter-subject in the bass (bars 21 – 24) :—

and a short episode (bars 36 – 40) in which the following figure is introduced :—

Both these patterns are used again in the final section of the sinfonia (bars 49 to the end).

INVENTION (Sinfonia) No. 14 in B flat major (p.74)

This is a happy, straightforward piece that Bach must have enjoyed creating. Probably it was improvised for one of his pupils in illustration of some particular point. This point may have been the use of stretti in which this sinfonia abounds.

Here is the theme which has a bell-like character :—

There is an exposition (bars 1 – 5) and a final stretto (bars 20 – 22). The middle entries are more in the nature of fugato, varying from single appearances of the theme to entries in stretti (bars 12 – 13, 14 – 16 and 17 – 19). This sinfonia has no regular counter-subject. An oratorical sense is provided by mounting harmonies leading to a descent from the high B flat to the final cadence.

INVENTION (Sinfonia) No. 15 in B minor (p.76)

There is a marked resemblance between this sinfonia and its corresponding invention. It is interesting therefore to make a comparison of the contour of the tunes and the arrangement of the keys. An individual feature of this sinfonia is the *bravura* arpeggio passage in bar three. This is later used episodically (bars 11 – 13 and 26 – 28) and forms a cadenza (bars 33 – 34) leading to the final cadence.

Here is the theme and its counter-subject :—

The entry of the alto voice with the theme in bar 7 is curtailed, and what follows is in the nature of an episode with the fragment of the theme used canonically with the upper voice.

Middle entries of the theme occur in the keys of the relative major (bar 14) and of its dominant (bar 17). The third entry, at bar 20, is again curtailed and is followed by an episode in texture like the first, with the difference that the arpeggio figures now ascend.

A return to the opening key is made at bar 30, with the suggestion of an entry in the middle voice.

The arpeggio figures need a light touch to gain the effect that one could produce on a clavichord. It is suggested that the right-hand notes of the chord with the pause, in bar 32, be spread.

C. Thornton Lofthouse

BACH'S USE OF THE PAUSE

It would seem that few musicians and music lovers are aware that Bach employed the pause in two unusual ways. We have this on the authority of his last pupil, J. C. Kittel (1732 – 1809), Haydn's exact contemporary.

When the pause is placed above the final note or chord, 'molto allargando' is intended. On the other hand, when it is found on the actual final bar line, Bach desired that only a slight 'allargando' be made. However, at the end of the 11th and 12th Two-Part Inventions and the 6th and 15th in three parts, we come across both these indications. One can but conclude that the intention here is both a slackening of tempo and a pause on the final note. Likewise, where there is no pause (as in many of his works, but not in the Inventions) one is presumably justified in maintaining the tempo until the end.

Kittel, however, seemed ignorant of the fact that Bach was not alone in these uses of the pause, for we find in the first copies made of Scarlatti's MSS (no original MS exists) that in his many harpsichord sonatas, Scarlatti employed the pause in exactly the same manner. In all probability, therefore, this was a generally accepted custom, knowledge of which has been lost or forgotten.

SOME OBSERVATIONS ON THE FINGERING

In undertaking the responsible task of fingering the Two and Three-Part Inventions one is faced by a number of contradictory yet co-related problems.

Several of these pieces lie uncomfortably under the hands in places, therefore patches of awkward fingering become inevitable. Another difficulty inherent in the text is that Bach rarely indicated any phrasing, exceptions being Numbers 3, 9 and 15 of the Two-Part Inventions, and in three places in Number 9 of the Three-Part Inventions. Therefore, except where the phrase outline is unmistakable through the presence of rests or of notes of longer duration, it is by fingering alone that it becomes possible to make clear the phrasing that the composer obviously intended. Hence, such occurrences as the employment of the same finger successively, and of fingering which, at first sight, appears both arbitrary and unnatural is quite unavoidable.

In addition, and conversely, we find sections where a normally obvious fingering might very well lead to a careless and casual rendering, so that, being faced with an unorthodox and unexpected fingering, the performer, as the result of the greater concentration entailed, the better retains and performs the passage in question. Then again, one is forced to resist the temptation of adopting a fingering that would completely obliterate those subtleties of nuance and duration essential to the performance of these pieces. Here and there, too, one comes upon passages where the 'legato' which the music demands cannot be executed satisfactorily, and in one place (bar 19 of the 14th of the Three-Part Inventions) only the hand of a giant could sustain to its given length the left hand F against the descending bass. In other tight corners, (e.g. the A minor Three-Part Invention), and in many closing cadences, the discreet use of the Right Pedal is called for. On no occasion can the employment of the Left Pedal be recommended to students.

Finally the performer should endeavour to play as one employing the piano with an understanding of the peculiar qualities of the clavichord and harpsichord, so that excessive speed, forced percussiveness, a vast tonal range, explosive dynamic exuberance, super 'legato' and sentimentality are all rigorously excluded. Only then is a close approximation to the intentions of the composer, (so far as we are able to understand them), at all possible of realisation.

Arthur Alexander

Two-part Inventions

Three-part Inventions

15 TWO-PART INVENTIONS

J. S. BACH

Though the MS. gives ⌇ in bars 1 and 2 ⌇ is generally preferred.

© 1956 by The Associated Board of the Royal Schools of Music.

A.B. 1137

See page 16 regarding
Bach's use of the pause.

A.B.1137

22

Bach's phrasing — probably because
he edited it specially for his son,
Wilhelm Friedemann.

28

In accordance with the custom of the time, the ♪'s on each main beat of this figure would be slightly shortened in value.

A.B.1137

32

(Vivace)

A.B.1137

Bach's phrasing

10

(Allegro ma non troppo)

(Moderato)

11

41

as at (a)

(release R.H.)

Bach's phrasing

(b)

A.B. 1137

(Allegro tranquillo)

(Andante con moto)

14

Bach's phrasing

(Allegretto)

15 THREE-PART INVENTIONS

(Moderato)

(Andante con moto)

(Allegretto moderato)

3

(Andante con moto)

(Andante piacevole)

A realisation of the embellishments found in the later copy of Bach's original 1723 MS.

* Other possible versions: *(b)* perhaps more suited to the modern piano

62

(Andante moderato)

(Allegretto amabile)

Bach's phrasing

68

(Andantino con moto e grazioso)

11

74

(Moderato tranquillo)

14

(Allegretto con spirito)

15